The Plague

Tod Olson

SCHOLASTIC INC.
New York Toronto London Auckland Sydney
Mexico City New Delhi Hong Kong Buenos Aires

Illustrations
Michael David Biegel

Printed in the U.S.A.

ISBN 0-439-12350-X
(meets NASTA specifications)

7 8 9 10 23 10 09 08 07 06

Contents

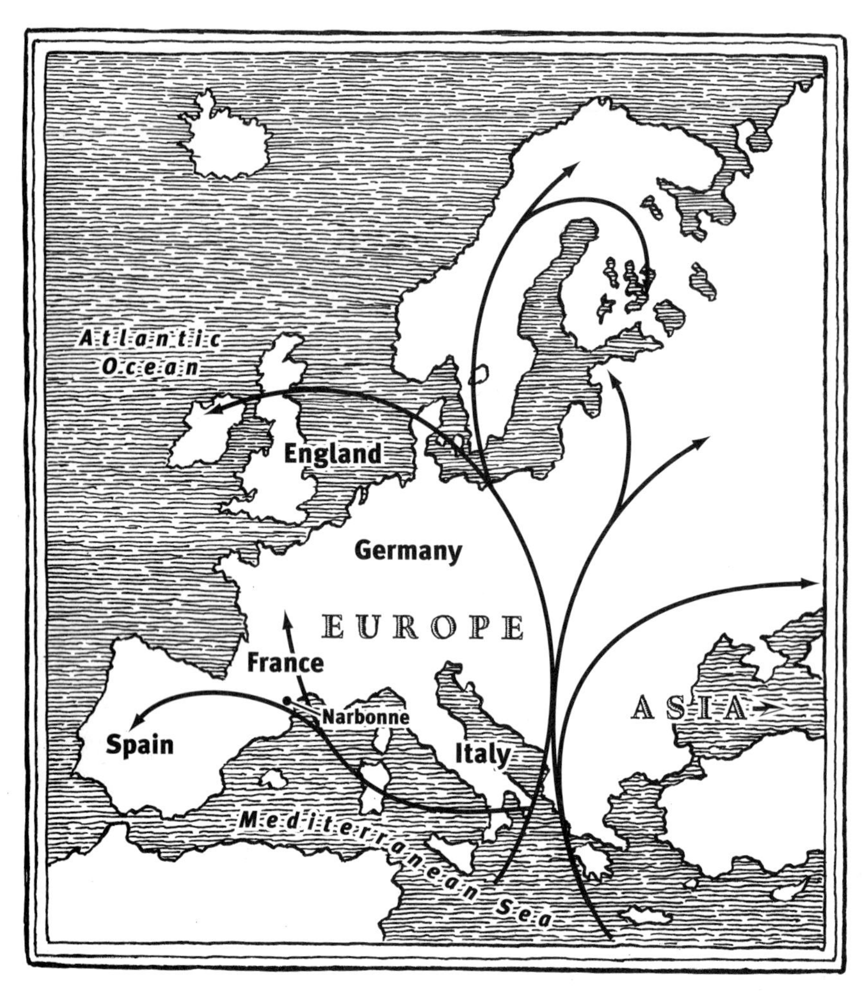

The plague started in Asia in the early 1340s. In 1347, it arrived in Europe. The disease first appeared in port towns on the Mediterranean Sea, carried by rats on trade ships from Asia. From there, it spread throughout Europe.

Introduction

Late in the year 1347, Italians began to die from a terrible disease. It started with fevers, headaches, weakness, and loss of balance. Then came the ugly swellings in the armpits. Horrible pain struck on the third or fourth day. Arms and legs started twitching. And the fifth day, almost without fail, brought death.

By 1348, this **plague** had spread to France, Germany, and England. Towns and villages all across Europe fell apart. At its height, the plague killed 800 people a day in Paris alone. Parents left their dead children on doorsteps to be carted away. Dogs dug up bodies buried in mass graves. Crops were left rotting in the fields. Sheep and cattle wandered till they dropped from starvation.

We know now that the plague was carried by fleas that lived on rats. But at the time, no one understood the disease. The best medical minds weren't even close to inventing a cure. (See "Avoiding the Plague," page 21.)

No one in Europe had any idea what to do. So they looked for people to blame. In many places, that blame fell on the Jews. Thousands were forced from their homes. Thousands more were killed. But, of course, violence did nothing to slow the plague.

The so-called "Black Death" had run its course by 1350. No one knows for sure, but it may have killed 25 million people. If so, between a quarter and a third of the population of Europe was gone.

This is the story of an ordinary kid caught in the middle of this disaster. Christophe is a 15-year-old living in the south of France, in a town called Narbonne. He's an **apprentice**, or student. He's agreed to help a surgeon do his work. In exchange, the surgeon—his "master"—is teaching him to be a doctor.

Christophe is fictional. But the events that surround him actually happened.

1

There was a time when I didn't think I would live to tell this tale. Even now, ten years later, I remember the smell of death as though it were just outside my door. And when I want to push it away, I remember Master LaRoche's voice. He was my master, my teacher, my friend. And I hear him telling me to open my mind, even when it seems too painful.

I was 15 when I saw the first victim. It was in the summer of 1348, the brightest of days. I was in the field to the south of town collecting herbs for medicines. I heard the sound of hooves and looked up to see a rider draped like a blanket over his horse. The horse walked slowly over the dirt toward town.

"You, there!" I called out. "Are you ill?" I was sure he was a trader who had come from the coast.

I got no answer and called out again. Still there was silence. I approached the horse and grabbed the reins. As I did, there was a terrible smell. The rider breathed in gasps. He was alive, and yet he stank of death.

Shaken, I left the day's work sitting in the field. I led the horse and her dreadful **cargo** quickly into Narbonne. It was market day, and the **merchants** and craftsmen were in the square selling their **wares**. People gathered around as I walked through. They were concerned about the man's health. But no one knew what it really was that I was bringing to town.

Jean Manon, the butcher's son, ran up to me and laughed. "Christophe! Your friend smells like our shop on a hot summer's day. You'd better salt him good before you sit down to dinner."

I managed a smile. "He'll be nothing but meat soon if Master LaRoche can't fix him."

"I saw your master this morning," he said. "I think he's helping someone on Tanner's Lane. That brown **mare** kicked a girl and broke her leg."

"Thanks," I said. I turned onto Tanner's Lane and found the right home. Master came out when he heard my cries. The rider groaned as we slid him onto the ground. His mouth fell open, and I could once again smell death on his breath.

Master LaRoche opened the man's shirt to give him air, and we gasped at the sight. Black spots covered his arms. His body appeared to be rotting like an apple. There were great swellings the size of lemons in his armpits.

Master LaRoche stood up and turned to me. His face was grim. "It is here, Christophe," he said.

"It?" I asked. "What is here?"

"The plague," he said. "Last month, you may remember, a trader came to town from Messina with a horrible tale. He claimed people there were dying like pigs."

"But we thought he was crazy."

"Maybe he wasn't," he said. His eyes looked past me into the air. "Maybe he wasn't. . . . Help me drag this poor man inside, will you?"

A great cloud shut out the sun as we were dragging him off. By the time we reached the door, the skies had opened. A **vicious** rain poured down around us. I pulled my shirt over my head as though the drops themselves might contain poison.

The next day, we left him on a pile of straw in Master LaRoche's home. My master told his wife to spend the day outside, to be clear of the foul air. She refused, bless her soul. She stayed behind to pack herbs and mud on the patient's swellings.

We went out to make our rounds. That evening, we returned to a terrible sight. The trader's swellings had burst. The black spots had spread across his body. I choked as soon as I breathed the air. Master LaRoche splashed vinegar on the body, and all about the room, to cover the **stench**. Then he threw rose water on the fire to **purify** the air.

We buried the man that night. I never learned his name.

2

Two weeks passed, maybe three, before I met Joseph. In those weeks, the plague had begun to spread its bony fingers around our town. At first, people refused to believe we were in danger.

Then, two Sundays after the trader's death, Charles the **tailor** stood up suddenly in the middle of church. He was sweating as he **staggered** toward the **altar**. His arms waved and twitched wildly. He made it to Father Marcus. Then he fell groaning on the floor.

I was too scared to move. I knew right then that whatever had killed the trader had escaped his body. It was in the air. Perhaps it was in the air in the church—the air I was breathing. I gasped and held my breath as long as I could.

Master LaRoche ran to the tailor's aid, along

with the man's family. In a minute, I made myself follow. For a time, the rest of the church did not move. Then, someone got up and hurried out the door. The rest began to run as well. Many of them covered their mouths as they left.

The next day, I saw my friend Jean Manon. "Did you see?" Jean joked. "That tailor looked like a goose fleeing the axe."

He was laughing. And yet, I had noticed that he had nearly run over a child trying to get out of the church.

But I was writing about Joseph. . . .

At first, I did not want to go. But Master LaRoche made me come along. The streets were empty, even though it was midday. Charles had died shortly after that day in church. And since then, the master and I had seen more than 20 victims. People were keeping themselves shut inside, thinking they could keep the air pure.

I could feel eyes peering out of windows.

"Master, it is against the law," I said nervously.

"To treat the ill?" he said and looked at me

with disapproval.

"Well, to bathe or eat or drink with Jews," I said.

"It is never against God's law—or any law I follow—to help people in need!" He began to walk faster.

"But what about the Christian children? Thomas, the merchant's son, told me they kidnapped a child in Avignon. Right under the **Pope's** nose! Then they nailed him to a cross, just like they did to Jesus!"

"Thomas told you that, eh? And did Thomas *see* it happen?" Master was angry now.

"No," I admitted. "He heard it from a trader. The trader had been in Avignon. He heard about it there. Everyone was talking about it."

"So, he heard about it from someone who *heard* about it from someone. And that person *heard* about it from someone else who probably *heard* about it too. We have a hearing problem in this land!" He was shouting now. A band of pigs eating garbage in the street looked up. They started and ran off.

"Why doesn't anyone believe in *seeing*?"

Master continued. "Isn't it better to *see* what is true—not just *talk* about what might be? In all of France, I bet you cannot find a single person who has *seen* a Jew murder a Christian child!"

"But if so many people have heard about it . . . ?" I asked.

"That does *not* make it true!" my master responded.

"I still do not think we should be going there," I said stubbornly.

"Christophe, when your parents brought you to me, I had my doubts that you were ready to learn the art of medicine. Your head was young. But I had always thought your heart was good." His head dropped. "The first victim of this terrible plague is human kindness."

We turned into the **Jewish Quarter**. A mad **flutter** of wings frightened me. Three crows disappeared into the dark sky. On the ground lay three half-eaten rats, dead in the street.

3

Joseph's house was as big as any in town. It was two stories high, made all of stone. His father traveled often to Milan to trade for expensive cloth. He brought it back and sold it to anyone with the money to buy. "Christians may talk about the 'dirty' Jews," Master had said on the way over. "But they are perfectly willing to trade with them or borrow their money when it suits them."

Joseph's mother welcomed us at the door with a warm smile. Around her neck hung a six-pointed **Star of David**, made of silver. In a darkened room at the back, her husband lay moaning on a bed. Her younger son, Benjamin, lay on a mat nearby. Joseph, who appeared to be about my age, stood quietly in the corner, eyeing me. Everyone in the family wore a small yellow circle of cloth on their robes. The law

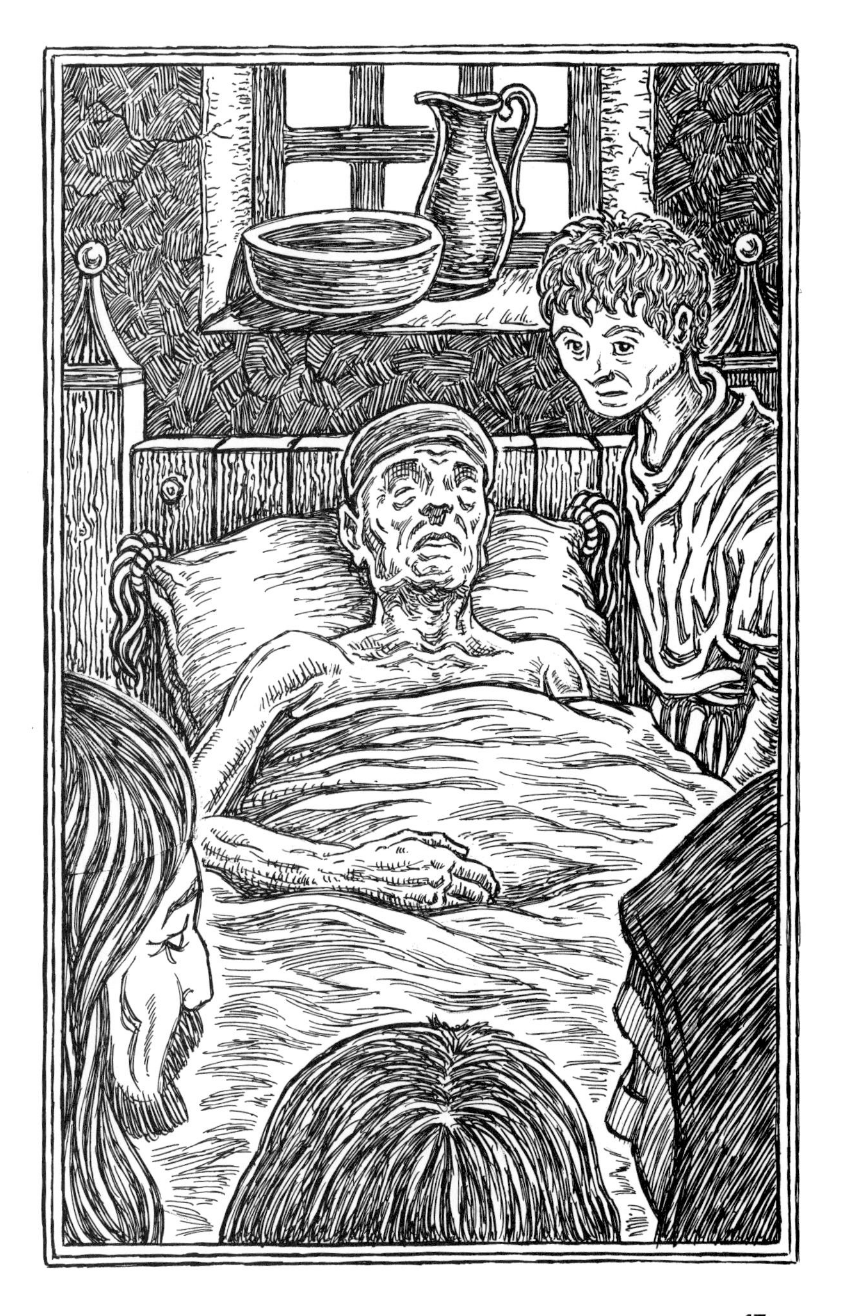

says they must, so that no Jew can pass as a Christian.

Master and I sat by the bed. I pulled the poor man's shirt off. I had seen it a dozen times, and I still had to choke back a gasp. The swellings were already the size of apples. It was as though something evil—something very much alive—had taken over his body. For a moment I could almost feel it escaping through his open mouth and into mine. A cold shiver ran up my spine into my neck. Then I made myself concentrate.

We washed the swellings. Then we packed them with a dressing of clay. We did the same for Benjamin and started to pack our bag. Joseph's mother began to weep quietly.

Suddenly, Joseph spoke. "You're not going to **bleed** them?" he asked suspiciously.

"No," Master said. "It won't help."

"But you must do something to cool the body," Joseph insisted.

"Cutting them will make them weaker," Master said. "I bled Charles the tailor. A day later, he was dead."

"What can we do for them?" his mother

pleaded. "Please tell me."

Master sighed and looked at his feet. "I don't know," he said sadly. "All our learning, all our books—nothing has prepared us for this."

"But, there must be something. . . ."

"I can only tell you what everyone knows. Eat onions, leeks, and garlic. Do not bathe; it opens the pores to let the poisonous air in. Keep southern windows closed; the disease is said to come from the south. Sleep on your side or stomach; it will keep the **vapors** from entering—"

"My older brother says bleeding cures," Joseph interrupted.

"Joseph . . ." said his mother, trying to quiet her son.

I could not keep silent anymore. "What does your brother know about medicine?" I asked. "My master is the finest surgeon in the south of France."

"My brother studies medicine at Montpellier," he said proudly.

"At Montpellier?" I tried to hide my surprise.

"Yes," he said, annoyed. "Even Jews can learn to practice medicine."

"I didn't mean—"

"My brother says we are the smartest students there," he said.

"I—I just didn't think they would be allowed," I stuttered.

"I guess there are *some* things Christians don't know," he said.

I was mad now. "We didn't *have* to come here! We could have . . ."

"Christophe!" Master called out. "Enough! Let us leave these people alone." He picked up our bag, grabbed me tightly by the elbow, and yanked me toward the door.

He turned to Joseph's mother from the doorway. He lowered his voice so Joseph could not hear. "I feel I must tell you, Madame Simon. I have treated two dozen people so far. Not one was still living a week later. I'm sorry." And we went out into the rain.

Avoiding the Plague

During the plague, there were almost as many theories about what caused the disease as there were fleas spreading it.

Some people blamed the plague on natural disasters. They said an earthquake had released poisonous gases from the earth. Scholars would try to guess the progress of the plague by studying the color of the sky or the shape of the clouds.

There were other theories. Moist air was supposed to carry the disease. So doctors told people to stay inside and keep fires burning. People fled marshy places for dry areas in the hills.

You weren't supposed to bathe or exercise. Both activities opened the pores to let the disease in.

Bad-smelling air was said to carry the plague. So when people had to go outside, they often held herbs or flowers to their noses.

If you got sick, doctors would pack your sores with mud and herbs. Or they'd bleed you to let the disease out.

So what if the plague happened today? Doctors would give their patients **antibiotics**. In addition, exterminators would be working overtime going after the rats and mice that carried the disease.

4

Thwack! Thwack! Thwack! The man next to me was beating his cane against the church **pew**. Philippe Martin was his name. He was a merchant. Light **flickered** off several bright silver bands around the stick.

Thwack! Thwack! Thwack! The crowd in the church began to quiet down. "I say lock them up!" yelled Martin in a voice like a crow's. "As soon as someone is **stricken**, lock him in his home!" The church started buzzing again, and he whacked his cane again.

My ear was beginning to hurt, when a great crash came from the altar. The church got very quiet. Father Marcus stood over the remains of a vase he had thrown on the floor. "Thank you," he said. "You cannot cure the plague by shouting it out of town."

He went on. "The town council has met.

They have passed some laws to limit the spread of the disease. From this point forward, all bodies must be buried at least five feet underground. The town gate shall remain tightly shut.

"Only outsiders with **essential** business here will be allowed in. Any unmarried man and woman living together must marry.

"Above all, we must follow God's word. And we must pray. Perhaps then He will have mercy on us."

Thwack! went the cane. "What about the Jews?" Martin cried out. I looked over. He was red as a tomato with anger.

Another voice from across the church called out. "They've poisoned the wells!"

I heard someone else yell, "Run them out of town!"

"Nonsense!" my master yelled, jumping out of his seat. "I have sat at the beds of at least ten Jews. They are dying as fast as everyone else. If they had poisoned the wells, would they be giving the water to their children?"

Suddenly, the red-faced man leaned over me. He lifted his cane and brought it down hard on my master's shoulder. He was muttering something I couldn't understand. Spit sprayed from his mouth onto my lap. He raised the cane again.

I stood up fast and caught his arm with both hands. Someone grabbed me and pulled me backwards over the pew. *Thwack!* I felt the sting of the cane on my arm.

I wrestled blindly. In a moment, I pushed my attacker onto the pew. I was shocked to find it was Jean Manon. He looked up at me with rage in his eyes.

Suddenly, a sharp tug at my arm sent me flying into the aisle. It was Master LaRoche. He pushed me toward the door.

We stepped out into the gray rain. I was hot with shame. My arm stung from the madman with the cane. We walked in silence for a minute. Then I said simply, "I am going home."

Master looked at me. "You are free to go at any time," he said. He sounded tired.

"You won't stop me, then?"

"You are nearly a man, Christophe," he said. "You will do what you feel you must."

"I can't take it anymore. Jean Manon was my friend—"

"When people cannot explain a tragedy, they must have someone to blame," he said.

We walked in silence. In a minute, we passed Jean Manon's street. His house was not far down, and I turned to look. At the door, I saw a strange-looking bundle.

"Come," my master said.

We walked up to Jean Manon's home. The smell from the butcher shop **mingled** with another all-too-familiar smell. I knew right away what I would find. I did not want to look. I did not want to breathe. If I ran fast enough, I thought, maybe I could outrun it. Maybe I could find someplace on earth that was free from this black death. Maybe I could stay alive.

Master pushed me gently forward. At the door lay a body, covered in a small blanket. I walked closer and made myself look. It was Jean's little sister, Marie. She just lay there, waiting for the grave digger to carry her off. There would be no **priest** and no funeral. She might as well have been a rat.

5

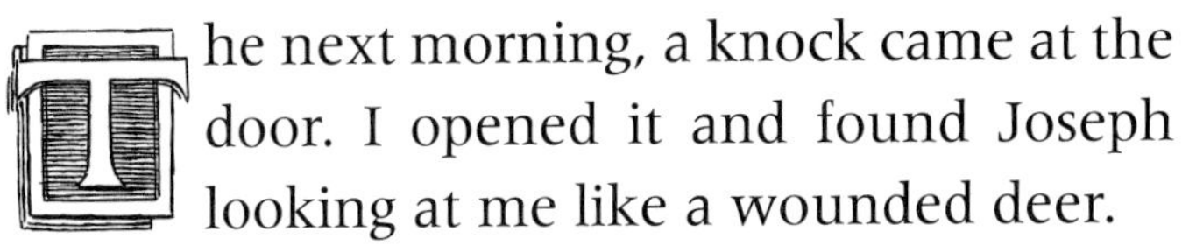

The next morning, a knock came at the door. I opened it and found Joseph looking at me like a wounded deer.

"Is your master at home?" he asked.

"What do you want with him?" I stood blocking the doorway.

"I—I need to see him."

"You should not be here," I said. "You'll put us all in danger." He did not move.

"Christophe!" Master LaRoche came up behind me. "Who is it?"

I stepped aside. They looked in each other's eyes for a moment. Then Master said quietly, "Your father and your brother?"

"And my mother as well," Joseph said, **wincing** just slightly.

"You are alone now?" Master asked.

"Yes."

"Well, come in."

Joseph stood for a moment. He looked at me as though I were a guard dog.

"Come in," Master repeated. Joseph slid past me into the house.

They sat on wooden chairs in the front room. I stood in the corner, **sullen**. For some time, Master asked questions. Joseph nodded or shook his head in response. All the while, he hung his chin on his chest. He would not look up. Was his family properly buried? Yes. Did a **rabbi** attend them? Yes. Did he have more family in town? No. Did he have enough food? No. Money? No. Did he have a place to go? No.

All of a sudden, he lifted his head. He set his eyes on Master LaRoche. "I want to learn to cure people of this disease," he said.

Master looked at him with sad eyes. "I'm afraid I can't teach you that," he said. "I would do better as a priest. Then at least I could comfort them."

"My brother sent word the other day," Joseph said. "They are performing **autopsies** at Montpellier."

"The Pope is allowing it?" Master asked. "Perhaps you will learn something after all. But you should study there, not here. Go where reason is stronger than **superstition**."

"I am young," he said. "They won't let me in."

"Well, I suppose . . . Christophe here is planning to leave us," Master said. "I am going to need help."

"You cannot!" I protested. Master **glared** at me. Still, I went on. "Christians will not want a Jew to treat them."

"Then it will be their loss," he said.

"But you will put yourself in danger," I said. "You saw what happened at church."

"Everyone is in danger now," Master said. "What does it matter if I add to it by doing some good?"

I looked at Joseph. Once again his head was bowed. He would not look at me. I pictured his mother weeping over his father's bed. And for a second, I saw my own mother's face in hers.

The air suddenly felt close and hot. I walked to the door. I pushed it open and ran out into the street.

6

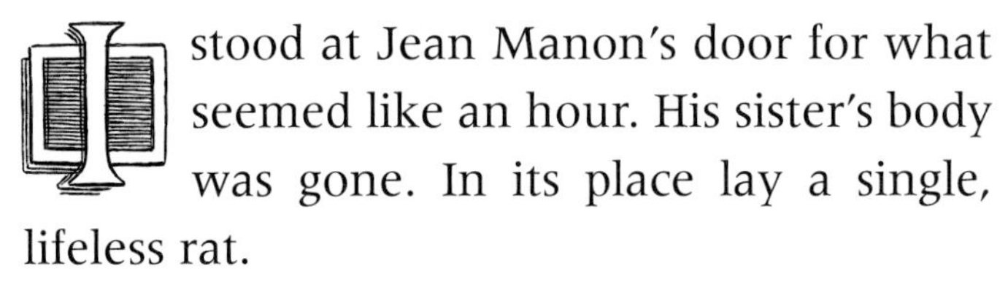

I stood at Jean Manon's door for what seemed like an hour. His sister's body was gone. In its place lay a single, lifeless rat.

Finally, the door opened. I had not found the courage to knock. Jean stood in the doorway. "What do you want?" he said coldly.

"I—I saw what happened to your sister," I said.

He just glared at me.

"Your father and mother?" I asked.

"Nobody else," he answered. "Only Marie."

There was silence for a minute.

Finally, I blurted out a stream of words: "I wasn't defending them. It's LaRoche who is friends with the Jews. It was his idea to help them. I only went along to please him."

I heard the words come out of my mouth

as though someone else were saying them. Shame began to rise through my body like **bile**. I wanted to run.

It had been two years since my parents had arranged for me to come here. Master LaRoche did not have to take me. He was known for miles around. He had his pick of apprentices. But he knew my father was ill. And he liked me. "Christophe," he said when my mother first brought me to town, "keep your eyes and your mind open, and we will get along perfectly."

Jean Manon spoke. "*They* did this, Christophe. *They* killed Marie. A rabbi in the north has confessed. It was a plot from Spain. A boy carried the poison from Toledo, and the rabbi put it in the wells around Thonon."

"Did anyone *see* him do it?" I asked.

"No one had to *see* it. He admitted it," Jean said. "Twelve others helped him do it. And they are not the only ones. Martin told my father he saw Balavignus the Jew lurking near the southeast well the other day."

"Martin? That's the one who tried to hack off my arm with his cane."

"He is a very successful merchant."

"A successful **brute,** more like it."

"You should be careful who you speak ill of," Jean said. "And be careful who you keep as friends."

"What is that supposed to mean?"

"Things will get hard for the Jews on their **Sabbath** this week," he said. "And there has been talk about your LaRoche." Jean's eyes were set like an **archer's** staring down a bow at his prey. I began to get scared.

"What kind of talk?"

"That he is helping the Jews," he answered. "Some say LaRoche made the poison that they put in the wells. Others say he has been cutting open **corpses**, even though everyone knows it is unnatural. And the vapors escaping from the bodies have spread the disease further."

I felt my ears get hot with anger. "They have no **gratitude**! Where are all the other surgeons? They're gone. Or they hide in their houses. They are cowards, like most people in this town. Even the priests refuse to see the dying. And what about you? I saw you run from the church as fast as you could when the tailor took sick."

"So did everyone else," he said. The evil look faded from his eyes.

"So did everyone else. . ." I repeated. I could not think of anything else to say. I simply turned and walked off. I left Jean Manon and the rat that lay where his sister once rested. And I walked.

I walked past the place where Charles the tailor once lived. I walked past Madame Bobeau's dogs, which no longer had an owner. I walked past a tiny wooden coffin the size of a small child. Finally, I came to the church and went in. It was dark and cool. I knelt in a pew and tried to pray, but my eyes would not stay open. I slept.

The Outsiders

When the Black Death arrived in 1348, people wanted someone to blame. They looked for **villains** outside the community. And in most parts of Europe, Jews were the outsiders.

For centuries, Jews had lived apart from Christians. They shared the same towns. But Jews lived in separate areas now known as **ghettos**. Laws often prevented Jews and Christians from marrying. In some places, Christians and Jews couldn't even drink wine together.

From time to time, Jews were allowed more freedom. They built temples and practiced their religion freely. Some Jews became skilled traders and made a lot of money. Most were educated.

But prejudice eventually won out. Some Christians resented the wealth of the Jews. Others believed rumors that Jews kidnapped Christian children and murdered them.

Around the 11th century, Jews began to lose their freedoms. Usually, they couldn't own land or hold public office. Taxes were high, yet most jobs were off-limits. Some places forced Jews to convert to Christianity. Others kicked them out altogether.

When the plague hit, rumors started flying.

People said that Jews had started the disease by poisoning the wells. In one small German town, 11 Jews were tortured into confessing. They were put to death. After that, towns in Germany and France began killing Jews or forcing them out of their homes. In one city, 200 Jews were herded into a wooden building and burned.

The Catholic Church did not officially support the killings. But the murders continued anyway. By 1350, Jews had been run out of nearly 200 towns. Thousands had been killed.

After the plague, it took 300 years for Jews to resettle in Germany. Then, in the 1930s, Germany—along with most of the world—sank into a terrible economic depression. Adolf Hitler and his **Nazi** Party came to power in Germany. And Jews were once again blamed for the country's problems.

From 1933 to 1945, Germans under Nazi rule herded Jews throughout Europe into prisons called **concentration camps**. There, about six million Jews were murdered.

The mass killings became known as the Holocaust. Six centuries had passed since the plague. And no one seemed to have learned a thing.

7

I awoke to the sound of dogs snarling and barking. The pew was hard. My back was sore. Light was pouring through the eastern windows. I stumbled down the aisle and out into the morning haze. A dozen or so men were walking quickly down the street. Four angry dogs led them, straining at their leashes.

At the front of the pack, I saw a familiar **gleam**. It was the walking stick with the silver bands. Behind it marched Martin the merchant. He struck the cane hard on the ground as he walked. It was target practice, I suppose.

I did not know for sure where they were going, but I felt a pit in my stomach. I ducked down a side street to get around them. Then I raced toward my master's house. I reached the door in several minutes, gasping for breath.

I burst inside and bolted the door behind me. The front room was empty. I walked to the back room and pushed the curtain aside. The sight struck me like a dagger. Joseph sat on one side of the straw mattress. Madame LaRoche sat on the other. Between them lay Master LaRoche, sweat beading on his face.

I walked up to the bed and took his hand. He didn't move.

"He's finally resting," said Madame LaRoche softly. "It happened shortly after you left yesterday. It began the same way it did with the others. The staggering. Then the arms twitching. Then the fever. Now peace for a while."

"It can't be! Not him." Even with death all around us, I had somehow thought that Master LaRoche's kindness would protect him.

It was as though she could see my thoughts. "The disease doesn't care," she said. "It is blind."

I looked at Joseph. For a moment, I was angry. He was here while I was gone. He had helped my master to his bed. He had held the cool cloth to his head. What gave him that right?

I was about to speak when a sharp **rapping**

came from the front door. *Thwack! Thwack!* And then the crow's voice: "LaRoche! Open the door, LaRoche!"

Madame LaRoche looked up, frightened. I stood up. "We can't let them in," I said. "They are here for Master LaRoche. Jean Manon told me. They think he helped the Jews poison the wells."

Joseph jumped out of his seat. He started for the door. I **lunged** at him and grabbed his arm. "What are you doing?"

"They won't come in here if they know he is sick," he said. "And they'll be content with me. They will have their Jew."

I let his arm drop and looked at him in shock. I could hear the dogs growling in front of the house. "But they'll put you in chains—or worse. . . ."

"What does it matter?" he said. He turned to say good-bye to Madame LaRoche. Then he disappeared into the front room and out the door. I ran to the window to see the dogs, teeth bared, snarling inches from his legs. The man with the cane stood in front of Joseph,

sneering at him. Someone else tied his hands behind his back with rope.

They led him off, and I began to turn away. Then I heard a dull thud. I looked back to see the **glint** of silver in the air. Martin raised his cane a second time. Then he brought it down hard on Joseph's back. I winced and turned away again.

8

I sat that day beside Master's bed and watched the room darken. I wanted so badly for him to wake and tell me what I should do. I kept hearing his words: "The first victim of this plague is human kindness."

I pictured Joseph in jail. And I could not stop thinking that it should be me. What would they do to him? Accuse him of poisoning the wells? Burn him alive? They'd never stop to question why he was trying to learn to cure a disease he had supposedly helped create. Or why he would let his entire family die of it.

It didn't make sense. I couldn't understand why Jean Manon and the others did not see. And how could I not have seen?

Jean Manon had said that things would get hard for the Jews on Saturday. What did that mean? It was now Thursday.

I sat long into the night, watching Master's face. Finally, I felt my doubt slip away. The great knot in my stomach disappeared. I got up quietly and slipped out the door.

The jail was not far from the church where I had slept the night before. I walked fast, thinking furiously as I went.

I passed Jean Manon's street and turned in. His home was quiet. I slipped around to the back and paused at the door. It was the north side, and a window was open. I climbed inside and looked around. I picked up a large knife and a heavy iron **crowbar** and threw them out the window. They clattered as they hit, and a dog began to bark next door. I threw myself out the window, picked up my **loot**, and ran.

At the jail, the first thing I saw was the cane leaning against the front wall. Martin and another man—the jailer, I think—stood talking quietly. I hugged the side wall and crept around back. A window with iron bars was cut into the wall at shoulder height. Inside, Joseph crouched in a corner on the straw floor.

"Hey," I whispered.

"What are you—"

"*Shhhhh.* I'm getting you out." I **wedged** the crowbar between the bars and the wall. Then I braced my leg against the wall and pulled with all my might. The bars creaked loudly. I stopped and held my breath. I didn't hear a thing. I tried again, but the bars wouldn't move.

I heard Joseph's voice in a whisper. "There are keys inside on a shelf. If you can get the men away from the door . . ."

I thought for a minute, then crept around the side. From the corner, I heard pieces of conversation.

". . . bodies in wine barrels . . ."

". . . send them down the river . . ."

". . . tomorrow night . . ."

". . . quite a bonfire it will be . . ."

Then there was laughter.

Bonfire! I turned and ran to the churchyard. My heart was racing. I started to gather brush and twigs in the moonlight. Load by load, I crept back behind the jail.

In a matter of minutes, I had a pile as high as my head. I returned one more time and

grabbed a torch. Even now, the priest was careful to keep one burning every night. I ran back and lit the pile. Smoke started to rise toward the sky. I ran to the other side and looked around the corner.

In a minute, Martin and the jailer began to sniff the air. They jumped up and ran around the building. As soon as they disappeared, I rushed inside. The keys were there. I unlocked the cell and Joseph ran out behind me.

We burst into the crisp fall air. Joseph ran. I looked down, grabbed the cane with the silver bands, and took off after him. We did not stop until we were standing in front of Joseph's door. I looked up. The night was lit by the moon. A million stars winked above. It had been a month since I found the dying trader. In all that time, I could not remember a single night of clear skies.

9

We sat at a large table in Joseph's house. Everything was exactly as it had been when Master LaRoche and I had been there.

We sat in silence for a moment. Then Joseph said, "How was he when you left him?"

"The same," I said with a sigh. "He didn't wake up."

"You know," Joseph said, "when he was crazy with the fever, he kept asking for his son."

"He doesn't have one," I said.

"He meant you."

I dropped my head and tried to swallow the lump rising in my throat. I looked at Joseph. He had torn the yellow circle from his shirt. Around his neck hung the Star of David that his mother had worn.

"You need to leave," I said suddenly. "I mean

all of you. Everyone in the Jewish Quarter."

I told Joseph what I had heard at the jail. We spent the rest of the night going quietly from door to door. Not a person was surprised by our news. Husbands woke their wives. Mothers woke their children. And they all prepared to leave their lives behind.

Everyone seemed to know without thinking where they would go. They were off to Montpellier and Marseilles, to Spain and to Africa. They would live with cousins and brothers and uncles and friends. It was as if they had always known. And they had never let themselves feel at home.

The next day was quiet. Once again, the sun was blinding. All across the Jewish Quarter, people packed their belongings. In the shelter of their back courtyards, they loaded wagons. They loaded horses and mules. They took what they could carry. The rest they left behind.

After darkness fell, the **procession** began. Women and children rode. Men walked.

Joseph and I stayed behind long enough to see the flicker of torches bobbing up and down, headed for the Jewish Quarter. We stopped and sat on a hill a mile from town. The torchlight mushroomed into a larger glow as houses began to burn.

I turned to Joseph and touched him on the shoulder. We rose, turned our backs on Narbonne for the last time, and walked away.

Epilogue

As I write, I am sitting in the library of the university at Montpellier. I am 25 now. Joseph sits across the table from me. The plague is gone. So is about a quarter of the people of France. Other lands have suffered equally. The disease showed no favorites. Young and old, good and bad—they all died in massive numbers.

When Joseph and I left Narbonne, we went to my mother's village. Somehow, it had survived. They lost only their priest, a baker's daughter, and three old women. My mother took Joseph in without hesitation and showered us with love. For three years, we helped her tend her sheep. Then we went to Marseilles to make our own way. Thanks to Joseph's brother, we are here. And in two years, with our eyes and our minds open, we will both be doctors.

About the Author

Tod Olson is a writer living in Vermont. He has written about American history and teenagers for 15 years. He has contributed to several illustrated books and many magazines.

Olson is also contributing editor at *Teen People*. There, he has reported on the Columbine school shooting, homeless kids, hate crimes, and other issues important to teens.

Glossary

altar *(noun)* a raised area or table used for religious ceremonies

antibiotic *(noun)* a drug that kills harmful bacteria to cure an infection or disease

apprentice *(noun)* someone who learns a trade or craft by working with a skilled person

archer *(noun)* someone who shoots with a bow and arrow

autopsy *(noun)* an examination of a dead person to determine the cause of death

bile *(noun)* a bitter green liquid made by the liver to help digest food

bleed *(verb)* to draw blood from someone as a medical treatment (a practice that was very common in the 14th century)

brute *(noun)* a rough and violent person; a bully

cargo *(noun)* goods carried by an animal or vehicle, such as a truck, ship, or airplane

concentration camp *(noun)* a camp where people are held as prisoners of war or political prisoners

corpse *(noun)* a dead body

crowbar *(noun)* a heavy steel or iron bar with a flat end that can be used to lift heavy things or pry something open

essential *(adjective)* necessary or vital

flicker *(verb)* to shine with an unsteady light

flutter *(verb)* to wave or flap rapidly

ghetto *(noun)* a section of a European city where Jews lived

glare *(verb)* to look at someone in a very angry way

gleam *(noun)* a beam or ray of light

glint *(noun)* a sudden flash of light; sparkle

gratitude *(noun)* the feeling of being thankful

Jewish Quarter *(noun)* the area of town where Jews lived

loot *(noun)* stolen items

lunge *(verb)* to move forward quickly and suddenly

mare *(noun)* a female horse

merchant *(noun)* someone who sells goods

mingle *(verb)* to mix together

Nazi *(noun)* the political party led by Adolf Hitler that ruled Germany from 1933–1945, known as the "National Socialist German Worker's Party" or "Nazi Party"

pew *(noun)* a long wooden bench with a high back in a church

plague *(noun)* a very serious disease that spreads quickly to many people and often causes death

Pope *(noun)* the head of the Roman Catholic church

priest *(noun)* a religious leader, often Christian

procession *(noun)* a number of people walking or driving along a route

purify *(verb)* to make something pure or clean

rabbi *(noun)* a Jewish religious leader

rap *(verb)* to hit something sharply and quickly; to knock

Sabbath *(noun)* a holy day of rest and worship in certain religions

sneer *(verb)* to smile in a hateful, mocking way

stagger *(verb)* to walk unsteadily; to stumble

Star of David *(noun)* a six-pointed star used as a symbol of the Jewish faith

stench *(noun)* a strong, unpleasant smell

stricken *(adjective)* overcome with a disease

sullen *(adjective)* gloomy and silent

superstition *(noun)* a belief based on ignorance or fear; trust in magic or chance

tailor *(noun)* someone who makes or fits clothes

vapors *(noun)* gases; in the 14th century, it was believed that substances in the body, called vapors, determined a person's mental and physical health

vicious *(adjective)* cruel and mean; harsh

villain *(noun)* a wicked person

wares *(noun)* things that are for sale; goods

wedge *(verb)* to split or force apart

wince *(verb)* to flinch or shrink back